GW00643853

Opposite page:

Hale Bopp over Wasdale and the mountains Yewbarrow, Great Gable and Lingmell.
Photographed by Linda Davison (Cockermouth Astronomical Society) on 8th March 1997 at about 3.30 a.m..
The sky was clear and moonless.
Exposure: 5 minutes at f 2.8 on Fuji Sensia 400 asa slide film, using a 50 mm lens and a driven camera.

The camera is mounted on a motorised drive that moves it, during the course of the five minute exposure, to compensate for the movement of the earth.
This enables a clear sharp image of the comet and stars to build up on the film.
This camera movement is the cause of the blurred image of the distant hills.
Where the slope of the hill just happens to coincide with the direction of movement of the camera the image is not blurred. This is most clearly seen on Lingmell; the hill to the right of the photograph.

Ron Kelton using the 16 inch reflecting telescope
at Trinity School Observatory

Opposite page:

Hale Bopp photographed from Watendlath.

Photographed by Linda Davison (Cockermouth Astronomical Society) on 28th March at about 10 p.m..
Exposure: 2.5 minutes at f 2.8 on Fujichrome Provia 1600 asa slide film, using a 135 mm lens and a driven camera.

This photograph was taken only two days before perihelion, the point of closest approach to the sun; a distance of 137 million km..

At perihelion the 30 km. ball of rock and ice was travelling at about 158,000 km/hour (98,000 miles/hour). It's coma or head was hundreds of thousands of kilometres across and its visible tail stretched back through space for tens of millions of kilometres.
It was estimated that Hale Bopp was releasing dust at 400 tonnes per second and water at more than 60 tonnes (18,000 gallons) per second.

This 135 mm image of the comet clearly shows the white dust tail of the comet which is produced by the Sun's solar wind. This dust trail is curved along the direction of the comet's orbit.
The blue ion tail is made up of charged atoms which spiral along the lines of the sun's magnetic field; hence the different direction.

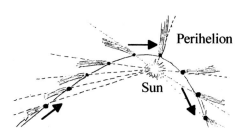

A comet's tail always points away from the sun

How can I take photographs (

All of the photographs in this small book are described as being 'driven.' '
movement of the sky. As a result any surrounding scenery, such as a tre
comet and stars are sharp and bright as the light from them builds up, dur
is often called a 'Scotch Mount' as the original design came from Scottisl
motors to drive them and can be home - made or bought. They are very p
be built for £20 to £30 by anyone with a modicum of ability in woodw
interest in astronomy generally, then you should consider joining you
below.

The reader will have noticed that all but one of the photographs in this b
Linda has produced more excellent photographs of the sky than any ot
subjects other than the comet. Anyone interested in purchasing prints of I
through the Cockermouth Society.

Border Astronomical Society

meet at 7.30 p.m. on alternate Thursdays from
September to April at the Trinity School
Observatory, Trinity School, Strand Road,
Carlisle, CA1 1JB. Meeting dates are displayed in
the observatory window and on the noticeboard
in the Lanes Library, Carlisle.

For further information, write or telephone the
Honorary Secretary :-

    David Pettitt
    14 Shap Grove
    Carlisle
    CA2 7QR   Telephone :- 01228 32724

Cockermou S

meet at 7-00 p.m c
month from Augus
Church Parish Hall, (
Information on r
Cockermouth Libr
Internet page.

For further informa
Honorary Secretary:

    Stuart Atkinson
    2 Horsman Street
    Cockermouth
    CA13 0HE   Tel

he sky like those in this book ?

ans that during the exposure the camera is moving to compensate for the
ppear blurred due to the camera movement. However, the image of the
exposure, on the same parts of the film. The device to 'drive' your camera
omers. Modern designs of Scotch Mounts often use low voltage stepper
is they can operate from a 12 volt car or motorcycle battery and they can
soldering. If you wish to know more and would like to develop your
amateur astronomical society. Details of Cumbrian Societies are given

re taken by Linda Davison of the Cockermouth Society. This is because
nber of the three local societies. Linda's astronomy photographs cover
stronomy pictures can contact her through the publisher of this book, or

---

stronomical

y

st Tuesday of every
lay at St. Joseph's
outh.
 is displayed in
 on the Society's

te or telephone the

01900 826139

Furness Astronomical Society

meet at 7.00 p.m. on the first Friday of every
month from September to July at Trinity Church
Centre, Abbey Road, Barrow in Furness.

For further information write or telephone the
Honorary Secretary:-
Richard Aldridge
56 Hartington Street
Barrow in Furness
LA14 5SR   Telephone :- 01229 826864

Opposite page:

Hale Bopp from Isel (near Cockermouth) looking towards Blindcrake.
Photographed by Linda Davison (Cockermouth Astronomical Society) on 9th April 1997 at about midnight.
The sky was clear and moonless.
Exposure: 2.5 minutes at f 2.8 on Fujichrome Provia 1600 asa slide film, using a 50 mm lens and a driven camera.

Linda can be seen in the picture viewing the comet through a portable telescope. The foreground was illuminated by firing a flashgun at a single point during the exposure.

Thin cloud can be seen in the sky. This was not apparent when viewing with the naked eye, but the film has picked it up due to the long time exposure.

The stars above the comet are in the well known constellation of Perseus.

Considering that the picture was taken at midnight, there is considerable light pollution on the image. This is probably from the town of Cockermouth and illustrates the need for local authorities to install the modern, full cut-off, high pressure sodium, street lights. These environmentally friendly lights cast more of the light where it is needed, on the ground. As a result less light spills upwards to be scattered by the water vapour in the air. The result is a darker and clearer sky for all of us to enjoy.

Opposite page:

Hale Bopp over Crummock Water, looking towards Darling Fell and Loweswater.
Photographed by Linda Davison (Cockermouth Astronomical Society) on 11th April 1997 at about 10 p.m.
The sky was clear with a three day old moon.
Exposure: 25 seconds at f 2.8 on Fujichrome Provia 1600 asa slide film, using a 50 mm lens.

The comet is in the constellation of Perseus.
The sky is quite bright as the photograph was taken in the north-west sky not long after sunset.

David Pettitt of the Border Astronomical Society demonstrating his weather satellite system at the Cumbria Fair of Science and Technology, held at Ullswater High School, Penrith.